FILM SONGS
Playalong *for* Alto Saxophone

Wise Publications
part of The Music Sales Group
London/New York/Paris/Sydney/Copenhagen/Berlin/Madrid/Tokyo

Published by
Wise Publications
14-15 Berners Street, London W1T 3LJ, UK.

Exclusive Distributors:
Music Sales Limited
Distribution Centre, Newmarket Road, Bury St Edmunds,
Suffolk IP33 3YB, UK.
Music Sales Pty Limited
120 Rothschild Avenue, Rosebery, NSW 2018, Australia.

Order No. AM992343
ISBN 13: 978-1-84772-388-8
This book © Copyright 2007 Wise Publications,
a division of Music Sales Limited.

Arranging and engraving supplied by Camden Music.
Edited by Sam Harrop.
Compiled by Nick Crispin.
Printed in the EU.

CD recorded, mixed and mastered by Jonas Persson.
Alto Saxophone played by John Whelan.

Your Guarantee of Quality:
As publishers, we strive to produce every book to
the highest commercial standards.
The music has been freshly engraved and the book has been
carefully designed to minimise awkward page turns and
to make playing from it a real pleasure.
Particular care has been given to specifying acid-free,
neutral-sized paper made from pulps which have not been
elemental chlorine bleached.
This pulp is from farmed sustainable forests and was
produced with special regard for the environment.
Throughout, the printing and binding have been planned to
ensure a sturdy, attractive publication which should give years
of enjoyment.
If your copy fails to meet our high standards,
please inform us and we will gladly replace it.

www.musicsales.com

Saxophone Fingering Chart

LIGATURE

MOUTHPIECE

CROOK

THUMB SUPPORT

BODY

1L — 2L
3L
1ST FINGER
4L — 5L
2ND FINGER
3RD FINGER
6L
7L
8L
9L

LEFT HAND

OCTAVE KEY

THUMB REST

1R
2R
3R
*4R
1ST FINGER
5R
2ND FINGER
3RD FINGER
6R
7R

RIGHT HAND

THE RING

* Not fitted on some saxophones

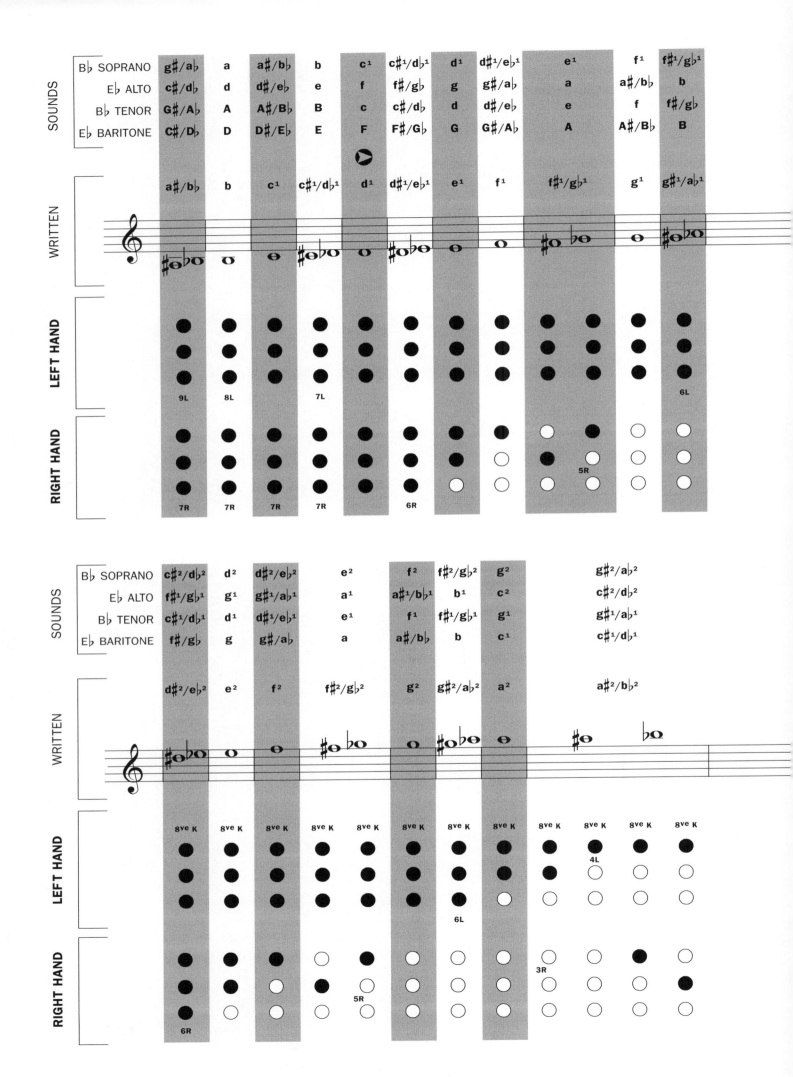

Indicates the lower limit of the best playing range

Indicates the upper limit of the best playing range

Born Free (Matt Monro)

Words by Don Black & Music by John Barry

Broadly ♩= 92

horns cue

With a steady beat ♩= 96

mf cantabile

mf

f

mf

cresc. poco a poco

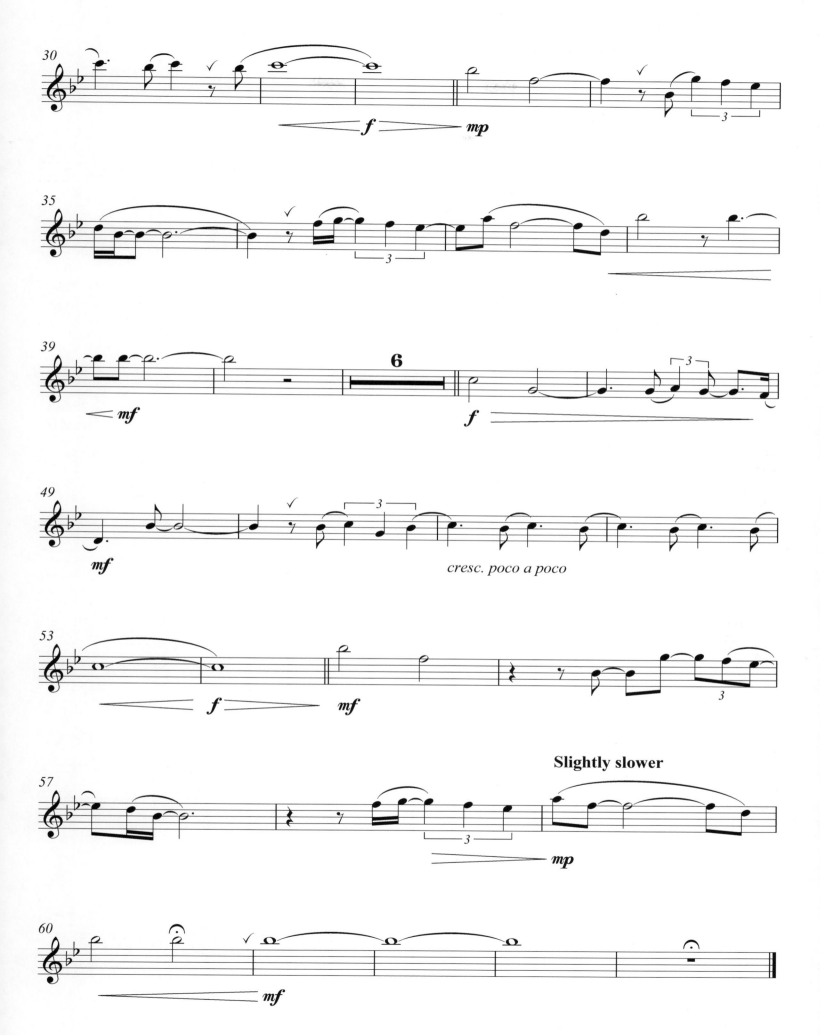

Georgia On My Mind (Ray Charles)

Words by Stuart Gorrell & Music by Hoagy Carmichael

Relaxed swing, straight quavers ♩ = 60

violin cue

mp espressivo

I Will Always Love You (Whitney Houston)

Words & Music by Dolly Parton

(I've Had) The Time Of My Life

(Bill Medley & Jennifer Warnes)

Words & Music by Frankie Previte, John DeNicola & Donald Markowitz

Kiss From A Rose (Seal)

Words & Music by Seal

Smoothly, with a lilt ♩ = 132

oboe cue

mp dolce

p   *cresc.*

mp   *f espress.*

to Coda ⊕

D.S. al Coda

Eye Of The Tiger (Survivor)

Words & Music by Frank Sullivan III & Jim Peterik

Nothing's Gonna Stop Us Now (Starship)

Words & Music by Albert Hammond & Diane Warren

With a driving beat ♩ = 96

Repeat to fade

Oh, Pretty Woman (Roy Orbison)

Words & Music by Roy Orbison & Bill Dees

cresc. poco a poco

mf teneramente

guitar cue

f

Ring Of Fire (Johnny Cash)

Words & Music by Merle Kilgore & June Carter

trumpets cue

mf

trumpets cue

mf

trumpets cue

Repeat to fade

dim. poco a poco

Stayin' Alive (The Bee Gees)

Words & Music by Barry Gibb, Maurice Gibb & Robin Gibb

With a Disco groove ♩ = 104

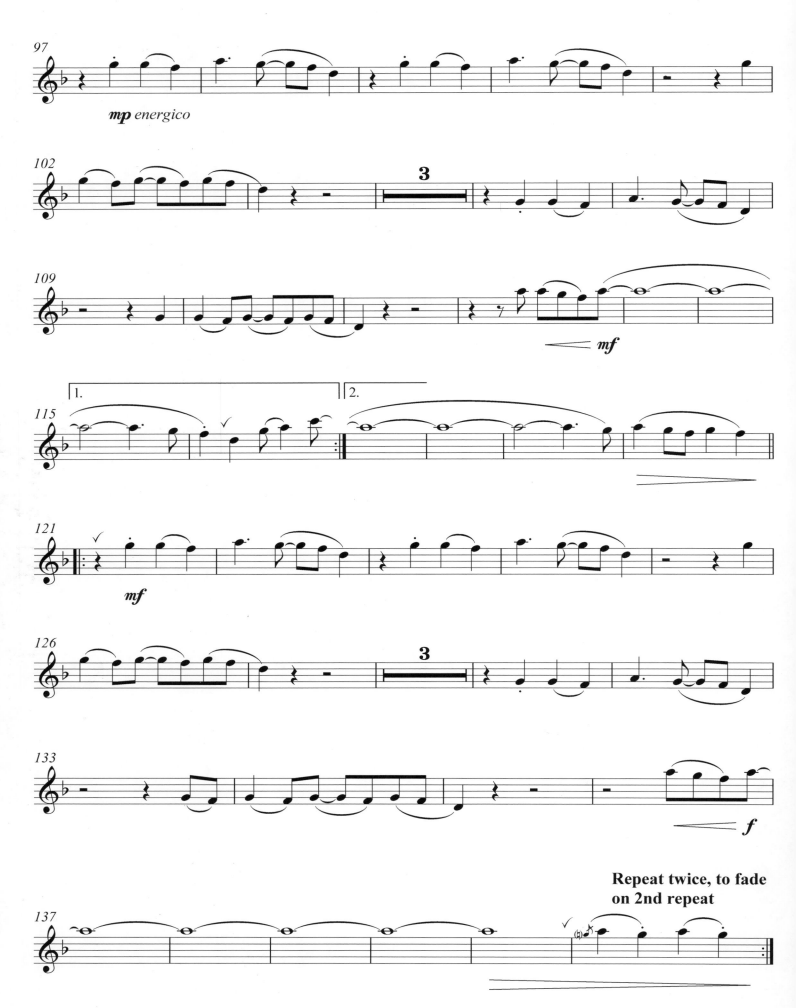

**Repeat twice, to fade
on 2nd repeat**

56789